CW00391633

THREE POTTED PANTOMIMES

IN RHYMING COUPLETS

by

Paul Alexander

Jasper Publishing
1 Broad Street Hemel Hempstead Herts HP2 5BW
Tel: 01442 63461 Fax: 01442 217102

Copyright; Paul Alexander 1994

THREE POTTED PANTOS is fully protected under copyright law
All rights, including; Stage, Motion Picture, Radio, Television, Publi
Reading, and Translation into Foreign Languages, are strictly reserve

To obtain information about acting fees payable on all professional an
amateur performances of these plays, together with any other detail:
please apply to the publishers;

Jasper Publishing
1 Broad Street Hemel Hempstead Herts HP2 5BW
Tel: 01442 63461 Fax: 01442 217102

A licence must first be obtained before any performance can be giver
and fees are payable in advance.

ISBN 1 874009 85 6

PREFACE

These scripts lend themselves to a wide range of uses. They could form the basis of a classroom, or junior school production, perhaps a monologue, memorised or with hand-held script. Also delightful late-night reading to a small child. An adult or junior drama group production, with or without the addition of costumes and properties etc., The possibilities are endless! You could even stage two pantomimes in one evening!

They have been devised for small performing groups where there may be limited stage facilities and resources. They can be readily adapted to suit circumstances.

They may be performed from hand-held scripts, when it is suggested that those taking part wear appropriate head-gear in keeping with the particular character.

CONTENTS

CINDERELLA

CHARACTERS

FAIRY QUEEN	Who also introduces the scenes
CINDERELLA	A princess under a spell
PRINCE CHARMING	An unconventional royal
LORD DANDINI	His aide and companion
BUTTONS	A lively page-boy
HORATIO BARON BROKE	A hen-pecked aristocrat
MATILDA BARONESS BROKE	The hen
LADY DAHLIA BROKE	] Their incongruous
LADY MARIGOLD BROKE	] daughters

SCENES

1.	**IN A WOODLAND GLADE**	Early one Summer morning
2.	**IN SPENTITT HALL**	Later that same morning
3.	**STILL IN SPENTITT HALL**	That evening
4.	**IN THE PALACE GARDENS**	Later that same evening
5.	**STILL IN THE PALACE**	Just after midnight
6.	**BACK IN SPENTITT HALL**	The following day

CINDERELLA

Scene 1

A woodland glade. Enter the Fairy Queen

Fairy Queen
> Greetings! I'm the Fairy Queen: I also introduce each scene.
> Giving you some information, though you must use imagination,
> For instance, this is understood, I am standing in a wood!
> It is the setting for Scene One, in which I have a bit of fun,
> By putting on a neat disguise, I give Cind'rella a surprise.
> For in a minute you will see, a poor old woman I shall be.
> Till then I'll have to disappear, because that girl is almost here.

Exit Fairy Queen. Enter Cinderella with bundle of sticks

Cinderella
> Hallo! My name is Cinderella. How I wish that some kind fella
> Would come my way and rescue me, from my life of drudgery.
> I work back there in Spentitt Hall: at everybody's beck and call.
> Baron Broke, he's not so bad, nor is Buttons, the page, a lively lad.
> In fact, he has a crush on me, but they're not nice, the other three!
> They drive me almost to despair;
> > "Do this!" "Do that!" "Come here!" "Go there!"
> I wish they wouldn't treat me so, I do my best to please them...

Enter Fairy Queen wearing a hooded cloak, taking Cinderella by surprise

> OH!

Fairy Queen
> My dear, there's no need for alarm. I am not here to do you harm.
> I have been searching all around, but no firewood to be found!
> I'll be in trouble, there's no doubt, for if my cottage fire goes out,
> I'll have no breakfast, tea or supper...
> Can't boil my kettle for a cuppa! *(encouraging an "AAH!" from the audience)*

Cinderella
> Oh what a shame! Don't be dejected *(offers bundle to Fairy Queen)*
> Please take this wood that I've collected.

Fairy Queen takes the bundle, puts it down and fumbles in her cloak

Fairy Queen
>You give me wood that I can burn, here is something in return.

She gives a dried up pea to Cinderella, who takes it and looks at it

Cinderella
>Thank you, but it's rather odd! A dried up pea out of a pod!

Fairy Queen
>Be not deceived by what you see, what you have is a magic pea.
>At some time when you're in distress, with things in a right old mess,
>Close your eyes, think of me, and make a wish upon that pea!
>Take care of it, and never lose it.
>The time will come when you will use it!

Cinderella puts the pea in her apron pocket

Cinderella
>I will remember what you say. But now I have to say "Good day!"

Cinderella exits. Fairy Queen throws back her hood

Fairy Queen
>There is something that you oughter...
>Know, Cinderella's my God-daughter!
>She is a princess 'neath a spell. One that was cast very well.
>And to bring the spell to end, this very day. I do intend
>However, not immediately, it will happen in Scene Three

Fairy Queen picks up bundle, then listens

>Again I'll have to move from here. There are others getting near.

Fairy Queen exits. Enter Prince Charming and Dandini

Dandini
>Your Highness, I don't think we should, linger like this in the woo
>Back at the Palace we're expected.
>That's where our way should be directed!

Prince Charming
>Lord Dandini stop your fretting. The time I say, I'm not forgetting

Dandini
>But we must make preparation, for tonight's Royal Celebration.

Prince Charming
>You mean that boring Palace Ball? It'll drive me up the wall!
>My parents, looking well ahead, have said it's time that I was we

So at this Ball I must decide, upon the one who'll be my bride.
Dandini
It is your duty as a Prince!
Prince Charming
The mere idea just makes me wince!
Although Dandini you are right, I don't look forward to tonight!

They both exit

Scene 2

In Spentitt Hall. Enter Fairy Queen

Fairy Queen
Here we are in Spentitt Hall, A stately home, but somewhat small!
The Baron and his family, have fallen on hard times, you see.
And are impoverished gentle folk, being by name and nature - Broke!
This is the place where Cinderella is a most unhappy dweller.
There is another servant who... *(pointing to wings)*
Will introduce himself to you.

Fairy Queen exits. Enter Buttons

Buttons
Buttons the Page-boy! Hi-ya folks!
I'm happy go lucky and fond of jokes!
I work for this family, but I conserve my energy!
There's Baron Broke, he's rather dim! The Baroness *(making thumbs down gesture)* She squashes him!
Their daughters, comic to behold, are Dahlia and Marigold!
Cinders works very hard, she's no slacker.
She's my dream-girl - she's a cracker!

Enter the Baron, looking downcast and carrying a letter

Baron Broke, you do look sad!
Baron
Buttons! I've had news that's bad! *(flourishes letter)*
From the Inland Revenue. My Income Tax is overdue.
And if it's not fully paid, a nasty threat here they have made.
They're going to send the bailiffs in,
Just when my funds are looking thin.

Enter Baroness, followed by Dahlia and Marigold

Baroness

There you are Horatio. I wish you wouldn't wander so.
When I want you, you disappear!

Baron

So much on my mind my dear. *(flourishes letter again)*
My Income Tax, it's in arrears!

Buttons

Been like that for years and years.

Baroness

(sharply) This is a private conversation!

Buttons

Thought I'd make an observation!

Baroness

Get out! Find some work to do!

Buttons

If I'm not needed - Toodle-oo!

Buttons exits, waving

Baron

Matilda, I mean what I said. Financially, we're in the red!
Taxes, inflation, rising prices. We're now in a family crisis!

Baroness

That matter can be soon put right, at the Palace Ball tonight.
The family honour we'll uphold. Dahlia and Marigold.
This function I have been advised, is being especially organised
So that Prince Charming can decide, upon the one to be his bride.
And if you two are on your mettle, perhaps on one of you he'd
settle.

Dahlia

Right Ma, I'll be the one to grab him!

Marigold

You won't! I'll be the one who'll nab him!

Dahlia

I'm the one he'll choose for sure,
When we glide round the ballroom floor.
As we trip the light fantastic...

Marigold

Make certain you've got strong elastic.
Part of your underwear might drop, the way you leap about and
hop!

Dahlia

When you dance, you twist and jerk!
You're like a cart horse - gone berserk!

Baroness

Girls! We'll have no arguments! Stop all this belligerence!
In this we all must be united, otherwise our cause is blighted!
Family honour is at stake, this opportunity we'll take.
At the Ball we'll cut a dash!

Baron

Matilda! We are short of cash!

Baroness

As aristocrats we'll hold heads high! *(grabbing his arm)*
Including you...

Baron

Yes dear, I'll try. But I'm not confident at all...

Baroness

(to Dahlia and Marigold) We must get ready for the Ball!

Baroness exits with Dahlia and Marigold. Baron follows

Scene 3

Still in Spentitt Hall. Enter Fairy Queen

Fairy Queen

That was Scene Two, and logic'lly, the next to come
Must be Scene Three!
Back to the same place we return, more of the story we shall learn.
But, now it's later that same day.
This time, that's all I have to say!

Exit Fairy Queen. Enter Cinderella and Buttons

Buttons

Come on Cinders, just for me, a great big S.M.I.L.E.

Cinderella

Buttons, you're so bright and breezy, but for me that isn't easy.
My attitude I'm not suppressing, my outlook is quite depressing.
Of social life I am left right out. I'm stuck here, never have a night
out!

Buttons

One night Cinders, we will go out,
Have fish and chips - a proper blow-out.
I'll save up money from my wages...

Cinderella

Buttons, you've not been paid for ages!
There's no way we could have that date...

Buttons
> There is, if you're prepared - to wait!

Baroness, shouting off stage, "Where is that Page-boy?"

> *(pointing to off stage)* I must go! Tonight they're putting on a show
> Dressed in their finery, coach and all, Got to drive them to the Ba

Buttons exits quickly, blowing Cinderella a kiss

Cinderella
> No romance, and no gaiety! Nothing for the likes of me!
> Do you wonder why I'm miffed? *(feels in apron pocket, and produce
> the pea)* What is this? That funny gift.
> The pea I got from that old dear. What she said was rather queer
> More than just extr'ordin'ry - make a wish upon the pea!
> And my eyes I'd have to close - I'll make a wish - I will - here goes
> What do I wish for most of all? *(closes her eyes)*
> I wish to go to the Palace Ball!

Enter Fairy Queen

Fairy Queen
> Cinderella!

Cinderella
> *(opening her eyes, and showing surprise)* Who are you?

Fairy Queen
> Someone who'll make that dream come true.
> Keep the promise that I made, this morning, in the woodland glade

Cinderella
> This morning? No. I am quite sure. We have never met before!

Fairy Queen
> Earlier I was disguised - That's why I am not recognised.
> I gave you the magic pea - now do you remember me?

Cinderella nods

> To send you to the Palace Ball, dressed like that, won't do at all!

Cinderella
> But I have nothing else to wear...

Fairy Queen
> Never mind - do not despair!
> With magical manipulation, I can make a transformation.
> By employing magic power, to last until the midnight hour.
> So until the clock strikes twelve, this role of kitchen maid you'll
> shelve.

To appear in your true worth, a Princess of the Royal Birth.
Princess Ella, you shall be, just leave everything to me!

Cinderella

This is fascinating - thrilling. To be a Princess I am willing.
It means tonight I'll be in clover...

Fairy Queen

When midnight strikes, it will be over.

Cinderella

But, until then, it will be bliss, an opportunity I will not miss,
Of mingling with that high-class throng...

Fairy Queen

Stop chattering, and come along!

They both exit

Scene 4

At the Royal Palace. Enter the Fairy Queen

Fairy Queen

At this Royal Palace Ball, a good time's being had by all.
With everybody having fun *(pause)* - well - not exactly everyone!
Ever since the function started,
The Prince, in fact, has been down-hearted.
Now things have come to a head, from the Ballroom he has fled.
Out into the gardens where, he hopes the pleasant evening air
His self-possession will restore...
The Palace Gardens - and - Scene Four!

Fairy Queen exits. Enter Prince Charming and Dandini

Dandini

Your Highness, why this sombre mood?

Prince Charming

Because Dandini I'm pursued. Being pestered and annoyed.

Dandini

That's why you're not overjoyed! Who is causing you this trouble?

Prince Charming

Two sisters - they're a shocking double!
Grinning, simpering, winking, waving. My attention they are craving.
Such attention is provoking...

Dandini

Sounds as if they both need choking. I'll arrange for their removal...

Prince Charming

Not possible to give approval.

As Palace guests they must remain - even though they are a pain!

Dandini

Your Highness, now you are out here, it's possible they won't appear.
To the Ballroom I'll return...

Dandini exits

Prince Charming

Peace and quiet is what I yearn!
All of this is such a bore, a wife I should be looking for.
I wish I knew my destiny. Might it be revealed to me?
What will be my future life? Where is she - my future wife?

Enter Cinderella. She sees Prince Charming and approaches

Cinderella

These Palace grounds are like a maze. So many paths - I'm in a daze!
The Ballroom I am looking for, but where it is I am not sure.
I'm sorry if you were disturbed...

Prince Charming

I am in no way perturbed!

Cinderella

I'm glad that you are not distressed...

Prince Charming

To meet with such a charming guest! Especially one who is alone...

Cinderella

That's true - I came here on my own.

Prince Charming

If, as you say, no-one has brought you,
Will you permit me to escort you?

Cinderella

Thank you. To that I agree. Please point Prince Charming out to me.

Prince Charming

That's a very odd request, from someone who is a Palace guest,
But, of course, I understand. You must come from a foreign land.

Cinderella

Not exactly, shall we say, I live a little way away.

Prince Charming

Can you not be more precise?

Cinderella

No. That answer must suffice.
A matter of diplomacy. I have to maintain secrecy.
One more request I'll have to claim, that you do not ask my name.

Prince Charming
> A most intriguing situation. I would like more information.
> I agree to your request. You will remain - my Mystery Guest!

Enter Dandini

Dandini
> Your Highness...

Cinderella
> You! You are Prince Charming?

Prince Charming
> I hope you don't find that alarming?

Cinderella
> I promise I did not deceive you...

Prince Charming
> Mystery Guest - I do believe you.
> And you agreed, as I recall, to be my partner at the Ball.
> I will not accept rejection, the Ballroom lies *(indicating, and taking her arm)* In that direction.
> It isn't very far away. Let us proceed without delay.

Cinderella and Prince Charming exit

Dandini
> Unless I'm very much mistaken, the Prince with her is clearly taken.
> He's certainly not melancholy, now he's met up with that dolly!

Dandini exits

Scene 5

Still at the Palace. The sound of a clock striking midnight is heard. Enter Fairy Queen

Fairy Queen
> In the Ballroom conversation, centred on that night's sensation.
> For, as the chimes of midnight sounded, everybody was astounded.
> Although not one word she said,
> The Prince's partner - stopped - then fled!
> He went to his apartment, where, he's thinking of his partner fair.

Fairy Queen exits. Enter Prince Charming

Prince Charming
> There is no reason I can say, why she had to act that way.
> We were dancing a quadrille, when she suddenly stood still.

As she heard the chiming clock, she was in a state of shock!

Dandini enters carrying one of Cinderella's shoes

Dandini - is there any news?

Dandini

(handing over the shoe) This has been found - one of her shoes!
A servant saw her trip, then stumble,
On the stairs he thought she'd tumble.
So he hurried to her aid, but she ran through the colonnade.
Through the doors, into the night, disappearing out of sight!
When he went back, on the stair, he saw that shoe just lying ther

Prince Charming

But this shoe she left behind, Dandini is a useful find.
A clue, which may well be the key, to open up this mystery.

Dandini

Your Highness, will you please explain?

Prince Charming

We can find that guest again!
Because you see, I have to trace her,
For in my heart I can't replace her.
A very simple matter - it's, to find the foot that this shoe fits!
We'll organise a fitting test. Visit every lady guest.

Dandini

A scheme your Highness which is smart...

Prince Charming

Straight away we'll make a start.
The guest list, we will have it checked.
Names and addresses we'll select.
I will draft a proclamation - you'll arrange its circulation.

They both exit

Scene 6

Back in Spentitt Hall. Enter Fairy Queen

Fairy Queen

Now we've left the Palace Ball, to come back here to Spentitt Hall.
And it is the following morning. Poor Baron, he is tired and yawning
He hasn't slept a wink all night, worried by financial plight.
Likely assets, he hasn't got 'em. The family is at rock-bottom!

Exit Fairy Queen. Enter Baron, Baroness, Dahlia and Marigold, talking

Baron

      Bankruptcy stares us in the face...

Baroness

      Nothing short of a disgrace!

Baron

      Disaster now we can't avoid...

Baroness

      Oh! Tragedy! I am annoyed!

      My rescue plan was water-tight! But at the Palace Ball last night,

      It became a total failure *(indicating sisters)*

      Thanks to Marigold and Dahlia.

      With them the Prince was not impressed...

Marigold

      Ma, that's not fair, we did our best!

Dahlia

      That's right! He's the one to blame.

      We tried - he wouldn't play the game.

Marigold

      We followed him, took every chance...

Dahlia

      He never offered us one dance!

Baroness

      In both of you I put my trust. But you failed...

Baron

      It means - we're bust!

The family take on expressions of unhappiness, as Buttons enters

Buttons

      What a lot of gloom and doom. Like a dentist's waiting room!

Baroness

      We can do without your views...

Buttons

      I've come with important news. D'you want to hear it?

Baroness

      Well what is it?

Buttons

      Any minute now - a visit!

Knock on the door offstage

      There it is, and right on cue! That was the knock...

Another knock on door offstage

      Knock number two! Wait a minute, then maybe...

Third knock on door offstage

>Yes, that was it. Knock number three!
>You never know, there could be four...

Baroness

>Shut up and see who's at the door!

Buttons exits

Baron

>The bailiffs, they are coming in. I think I need an aspirin!

Baroness

>You don't. Calm down Horatio. Cool indifference we will show.
>Even though this is alarming...

Buttons enters

Buttons

>A Royal Visitor - Prince Charming!

Prince Charming enters followed by Dandini, who is carrying the shoe

Dandini

>The Prince has come to visit you. Please look at this dainty shoe
>The one you now see here displayed *(holds up shoe)*
>At last night's Ball it was mislaid.
>Incidentally, I must mention, it is the Prince's clear intention,
>Whoever's foot it occupied, that lady will become his bride.

Dahlia and Marigold jostle each other

Marigold

>You know, I thought that I had lost it, luckily you've come across

Dahlia

>Not her's. That shoe belongs to me. I recognised it instantly!

Marigold

>That shoe fit you? Don't make me laugh.
>The size you take - ten and a half!
>Feet like yours - big and fat...

Dahlia

>Hark who's talking - yours are flat. Suitable for hob-nail boots...

Marigold

>*(lunging at Dahlia)* I'll pull your hair out by the roots!

Baroness moves between them

Baroness

    Idiots! You make me furious!

Prince Charming

    It's obvious those claims were spurious.

    Our search must still be undertaken...

Prince Charming and Dandini are about to exit, when, enter Fairy Queen

Fairy Queen

    No! Prince Charming. You're mistaken.

    The rightful owner of the shoe, and of your heart, I bring to you!

Fairy Queen indicates to the wings. Enter Cinderella to on-stage reaction

Baroness

    Rubbish! Some trick is being played. That girl is our kitchen-maid.

Marigold

    She's not aristocracy...

Dahlia

    She's a common nobody!

Fairy Queen

    Silence! I'll have no more of this!

    (gesturing to Baroness, and sisters) The three of you. Get out!

    Dismiss!

As in a trance the Baroness and sisters exit, watched by an amused Buttons, and an amazed Baron

    (to Dandini) Fit the shoe! Proof there will be...

Buttons supports Cinderella. Dandini fits the shoe, kneeling, then standing up

Dandini

    Your Highness, it fits perfectly!

Fairy Queen

    My God-daughter, Princess Ella. Had I the time then I would tell a

    Tale of how a spell was cast, but it is all now in the past.

    And can be safely set aside...

Prince Charming

    Princess, you'll be my honoured bride.

Buttons

    Cinders! Sorry, I mean Princess. You'll be changing your address.

    And need a Page-boy of your own. There is one who is well-known.

    He is highly qualified, and is standing by your side.

Cinderella

> *(to Prince)* I'm sure that I have your permission,
> To offer Buttons that position?

Buttons

> Say "Yes" Prince. Don't be a meanie...

Prince Charming

> *(laughing)* Of course, arrange that with *(indicates)* Dandini!

All exit except Fairy Queen and Baron

Baron

> *(moving to Fairy Queen)* Madame! My congratulations.
> On your magic conjurations!
> My wife and daughters you have quelled
> *(confidentially)* D' you think like that they could be held?

Fairy Queen

> Baron, you recognise my powers. Let this little secret be ours.
> *(making a magic pass over his head)*
> Henceforth be Master in the Hall, and those bailiffs, they'll not ca'
> All those debts of yours, you'll pay. A fortune soon will come you
> way.

Baron

> A thousand thanks! I am delighted...

Fairy Queen

> *(to audience)* My duty is to see wrongs righted.
> Turning any tears to laughter. When all live - happy ever after.

Fairy Queen indicates to the wings, rest of cast return to make final bou

JACK AND THE BEANSTALK

CHARACTERS

FAIRY QUEEN	Who also introduces each scene
LILY WHITE	A hard-up widow
JACK WHITE	Her son
MATT WHITE	Her other son
SEBASTIAN GRAY	Her landlord - the local Squire
ALICE	Her friend - a village gossip
ROSE	Another friend and gossip
PRINCESS MIRABEL	Kidnapped by a giant
ADELAIDE	Her outspoken maid
THE GIANT	Offstage voice - heard but never seen

SCENES

1.   **ON A VILLAGE GREEN IN TERRANIA**

2.   **IN A STREET ELSEWHERE IN THE VILLAGE**

3.   **IN THE GIANT'S CASTLE IN CLOUDLAND**

4.   **BACK ON THE VILLAGE GREEN**

5.   **STILL ON THE VILLAGE GREEN**

JACK AND THE BEANSTALK

Scene 1

On the Village Green in Terrania. Enter the Fairy Queen

Fairy Queen
Greetings to you, one and all. I am the Fairy Queen.
As well as that you'll find that I will introduce each scene.
I shall appear, from time to time, providing information,
And ask that in this pantomime you'll use imagination.
A fascinating story is this one that we will tell,
It starts here on this Village Green, in Delving-in-the-Dell.

Indicating stage right

In a cottage over there, and slightly to the right.
There lives a widow, who's hard up. Her name is Lily White.
She has two sons, called Matt and Jack, a happy family.
But better off, with cash to spare, is what they'd like to be.

Indicating stage left

In contrast, and in Manor House, just there across the way.
Resides their landlord, very rich, Sebastian Squire Gray.
A selfish man, his only aim, his fortune to increase.
Needless to say that Squire Gray's the villain of the piece.
What follows then will be Scene One, for which I've set the scene.
Which means that for the present, it is - exit Fairy Queen.

Fairy Queen exits, stage right. Enter, also from stage right, Lily and Jack

Lily White
Hello, I am Lily White...
Jack
And I am Jack, her son.
Lily White
He is not an only child - I have another one.
His proper name is Matthew, but he is known as Matt.
And at first no doubt you'd say, there's nothing wrong in that.
The trouble is the name Matt White, some people think is quaint.
Just because they've seen it printed, on a tin of paint!

Jack

Matt is not here with us, he is at the market now.
We need to raise some money, so we've got to sell our cow.

Lily White

Old Dora, well she had to go. A pity to be sure.
We didn't want to do it, but we had to, 'cos we're poor.
We'd like a bit of sympathy, and that deserves an "AAH"

Lily and Jack encourage the audience to "Aah"

And in return, from us to you, here comes our answer...

Lily and **Jack**

(together) TA!

Squire Gray enters, stage left

Squire Gray

Widow White, I was about to call on you today.
I am glad I've met you...

Lily White

It's me landlord, Squire Gray!

Squire Gray

You may not be aware of it, but I am telling you.
A little matter of the rent - it's six weeks overdue!

Lily White

Six weeks? Six weeks? That cannot be! That much I cannot owe
you...

Squire Gray

(producing rent-book) I'm positive! It's definite! The evidence I'll show
you!

Squire Gray taps the open rent-book. Lily White looks at it

Lily White

Jack, he's right! It is a lot! And I can't pay this morning...

Squire Gray

(putting book away) As I suspected Widow White. Very well, a
warning.
You've seven days in which to pay, and if it's not collected,
From your cottage, all of you, are going to be ejected!.

Jack

If you'll excuse me Squire Gray, the word should be "evicted".

Squire Gray

(angrily) Look here, by riff-raff such as you I won't be contradicted
I've always thought no good would come of widespread education

The lower orders simply gain ideas above their station.
I'm sure my meaning is quite clear, of that I have no doubt.
If that back rent's not paid in full, then you will be chucked out!

Squire Gray exits, stage left

Jack

We're in a fix! I only hope that something turns up Mother...

Lily White

(looking to off stage right) It's going to, almost at once,
For here comes Matt, your brother!

Matt enters, stage right

Jack

From the market you've returned. And you are minus Dora...

Lily White

We need some cash, and so I hope you got a good price for her.

Matt

I tried to sell her, Ma, I did. I did my level best,
But everybody shook their heads, with her they weren't impressed.
Then as I was on my way home, along came this old hag.
(producing small bag) She said that she would take the cow,
If I would take this bag.
She told me she would guarantee a fortune could be gained
By anyone who had the sense to use what it contained.

Lily White

So tell us what there is inside. Matt, what did you get?

Matt

Don't know Ma, because you see, I've not looked in it yet.

Lily White

Let's see this fortune you have got. Come on, give it here...

She takes the bag and looks inside

Jack

Mother, what's inside the bag?

Lily White

Oh dear! Oh dear! Oh dear!
Your brother Matt's been really conned. Tricked by that old hag.
No way a fortune could be gained by what is in this bag.

Matt

I've been diddled? Taken in?

Jack

That's what mother means...

Lily White

> *(showing them the open bag)* There is nothing in this bag, except
> some mouldy beans.
> Not one bean is any good. There's no way we could grow 'em.
> We'll give them to that mouldy Squire, *(moving to stage right)*
> On his estate I'll throw 'em.

She throws the bag off stage

Matt

> Sorry Ma! I thought I'd made a useful swap for Dora...

Jack

> It means that now we've lost our cow, our family is poorer.

Lily White

> Don't remind me of it Jack, for by this time next week,
> We'll be even poorer still - completely up the creek!

They all exit stage right

Scene 2

A street elsewhere in the village. Enter Fairy Queen

Fairy Queen

> Something I forgot to tell, and now I will explain here,
> This village is located in a country called Terrania.
> King Claud is most unhappy, and he could not be distraughter.
> Ever since he heard about the kidnap of his daughter.
> She was whisked away to Cloudland, that's a region in the sky,
> By a cruel and evil giant, to his castle way up high.
> Scene Two, still in the village, now we're in a nearby street,
> And two more people in this tale, we are about to meet.

*Fairy Queen exits, stage right. Enter Alice and Rose with shopping basket
talking*

Alice

> Remember Rose, what I've told you must never be revealed.

Rose

> Alice, you can rely on me, my lips are firmly sealed.
> I mean, to break a confidence, that would be downright silly...

Alice

> We'll keep it just between ourselves...

Rose

> We will...

Enter Lily White, stage right

Alice

Good morning Lily.
Not heard the latest I suppose, but keep this confidential...

Lily, just between ourselves, remember, it's essential.

The three move close together, whispering

Rose

Yes, you know the one I mean, the one who lived next door.

Lily

She never did! I am surprised! Rose, are you quite sure?

Alice

Through her front-room window several people said they'd seen her.

Lily

You do surprise me Alice...

Rose

And there was the window-cleaner...

Alice

She gives you the impression she's as pure as driven snow...

Rose

Hmm! Still waters running deep...

Lily

It only goes to show!

Enter Jack with handbill, stage right

Alice

Is that another notice Jack, from King Claud at the Palace?

Jack

Yes, the very latest, just been sent out Alice.

Rose

The King must still be hoping the Princess will be released.

Jack

The reward that he has offered is now to be increased.
One hundred thousand crowns, that's what he's prepared to pay.

Lily

If only just a bit of that amount could come our way!

Alice

But the Princess is in Cloudland, out of reach up in the air.

Jack

(looking up) I would try to rescue her, if I could get up there.
But I don't know how to do it. As far as I'm concerned,
The reward is also out of reach, and by me can't be earned.

Matt enters, running and out of breath, stage left

Matt

Back there! Back there! *(starts to pant)*

Lily

You're out of breath...

Matt

There, on the Village Green!
It's gigantic, it's enormous...

Lily

Well, I wonder what he's seen?

Matt

A beanstalk! It's a whopper! I could not believe my eyes!
I've never known a beanstalk to grow to such a size.
I tell you it is massive! You should see the height!
It's growing up into the clouds! The top is out of sight!
It's there on Squire Gray's estate *(pointing off stage)*
Where Ma you threw those beans...

Jack

There is an explanation. I know exactly what this means.
Matt, you will remember, the words of that old hag.
She said a fortune could be gained with what was in that bag.
The means to get to Cloudland - that's what we possess.
We can try for the reward - and rescue the Princess.
One hundred thousand crowns, the fortune, that's what is at stake.
Matt, if you'll come with me, there is a route that we can take.

Matt

I was not successful when I went to sell our cow.
But I see that I have a chance to do much better now.
Right-ho Jack, I'll go with you...

Alice

What courageous lads you are!

Lily

I know they both are doing this to help their dear old Ma.

Jack

Let's strike while the iron is hot. Matt, let's not waste more time.
But hurry to the Village Green. That beanstalk we will climb

All exit, stage left

Scene 3

The Giant's Castle in Cloudland. Enter the Fairy Queen, stage right

Fairy Queen
>We too now go to Cloudland, where in the Giant's stronghold,
>The next part of this story, to you is being told.
>We'll meet the kidnap victims, the Princess Mirabel,
>Together with her personal maid, who is up there as well.

Fairy Queen exits, stage right. Enter Princess Mirabel and Adelaide, stage left

Adelaide
>Princess, I have a question. I am home sick for Terrania,
>That is where I ought to be, how long must we remain here?

Mirabel
>I have to say with honesty, I am very much afraid,
>The answer to that question I do not know, Adelaide.
>We must both be patient, for home both of us are pining.
>Do not forget that every cloud has got a silver lining.

Adelaide
>Up here the place is full of clouds, dozens all around us.
>Isn't it a pity not one silver lining's found us!

Mirabel
>I am certain if we wait, a rescuer will find us.
>To Terrania we'll return, with all of this behind us.

Adelaide
>Princess, you're optimistic, but we're too far off the ground.
>To get up here to Cloudland some method must be found.
>I think it is impossible, no-one could be that clever,
>If you ask me, then I would say, we'll be up here forever!

Mirabel
>*(looking off stage left)* Something strange has just appeared,
>Outside the castle wall.
>I can see it through the cloud. It's green, and very tall.
>I'm going to take a closer look. I will investigate...

Adelaide
>Shall I come too?

Mirabel
>No Adelaide. You stay in here and wait.

Princess Mirabel exits, stage left

Adelaide

    Suits me. There's nothing much to do, so I don't mind waiting.
    I wonder what it was she saw? Is she hallucinating?
    I mean, the life we live up here is horrible, not jolly.
    It wouldn't be surprising if she's going off her trolley.
    Look at me, I'm far from pleased, I'd not be in this mess,
    If, when she was kidnapped, I'd not been with the Princess.
    Here I am in Cloudland, well and truly stuck!
    I should have known, my horoscope said I'd have bad luck!

Princess Mirabel enters with Jack and Matt

Mirabel

    What I saw was a beanstalk. These are Matt and Jack.
    They've climbed up from Terrania. They are going to take us back.

Adelaide

    Very pleased to meet you. We'd better go without delay.
    I don't think we should hang about, so let's be on our way.

Mirabel

    To go out to the beanstalk now, that would be opportune.
    The Giant will now be dozing. He sleeps every afternoon.

Matt

    We don't wish to meet him. I am glad that he is snoring.

Giant

    (off stage, using an amplified tape recording)
    FE-FI-FO-FUM! I SMELL THE BLOOD OF TERRANIANS!

Adelaide

    No! The Giant is not asleep!

Matt

    We know! We heard him roaring!
    I didn't like the sound of that. He sounds a bit annoyed!

Jack

    An angry Giant, a danger we must certainly avoid.

Mirabel

    Yes, he is not happy, and from what we know of him,
    He will try to catch us, and tear us limb from limb!

Jack

    We heard he was unpleasant, with an ugly reputation...

Adelaide

    Excuse me. I would like to make an urgent observation.
    The Giant is getting closer, I'm suggesting, I'm not hinting,
    Never mind this casual chat, it's time that we started - sprinting.

They all exit quickly, stage left, as the Giant roars again

Giant

(off) FE-FI-FO-FUM! I SMELL THE BLOOD OF TERRANIANS!

Scene 4

Back to the Village Green. Fairy Queen enters, stage right

Fairy Queen

They are heading for the beanstalk, up there in Cloudland's space.
But something has been happening, down at the beanstalk's base.
And back to the Village Green, for Scene Four we return,
What exactly happened, you are now about to learn.

Fairy Queen exits, stage right. Enter Lily White, Alice and Rose, stage right. They stop and look up

Lily White

They could be facing danger, while they're up in the air.
I know they are courageous, but I hope they're taking care.

Alice

I know that you are worried, but I'm sure they're safe and sound.
You'll be feeling better when they're back here on the ground.
All of us would like to know how they are getting on.

Rose

(pointing off stage left) Lily! Alice! Over there!
Look! The beanstalk's GONE!

They begin to move to off stage left. Enter Squire Gray, stage left, who stops them

Squire Gray

Where do you think you're going? My estate is private land.
None of you can come inside. All villagers are banned.

Lily White

There was a beanstalk growing there...

Squire Gray

I know. I never grew it...

Alice

Squire Gray, we'd like to know, what has happened to it?

Squire Gray

That beanstalk was a noxious weed. Needing prompt attention.
It was a blot on the landscape...

Lily White

Just like someone I could mention!

Squire Gray

> Consequently I decided I would make some alteration,
> By applying a technique of horticultural amputation.
> To make it simple for you - I sharpened up my axe
> Dealt with that wretched beanstalk, I gave it several whacks.

Rose

> Squire Gray! You chopped the beanstalk down? A wicked thing to
> do.

Lily White

> You should have left the beanstalk...

Squire Gray

> What has it got to do with you?

Lily White

> My lads climbed up to Cloudland. They're after the reward,
> For the rescue of the Princess, being offered by King Claud.
> And now you've cut the beanstalk down they can't get home again.
> It means that up in Cloudland forever they'll remain!

Squire Gray

> That is not my problem, if they are in a fix,
> They've only got themselves to blame by stupid climbing tricks.
> What's done is done. It's over - nothing further to discuss.
> *(making a dismissive gesture)* Clear off! Get right away from here!
> Stop making all this fuss!

Squire Gray exits, stage left

Alice

> He really is a horrid man! How can he be so callous?

Lily White

> I'll never see my lads again! How will I manage Alice?
> Now I will be on my own, without my family.

They all move to exit, stage right

Rose

> Thanks to wicked Squire Gray, this is a tragedy.

Scene 5

Still on the Village Green. Enter Fairy Queen, stage right

Fairy Queen

> This is not the situation that the author was intending.
> He had made provision for the usual happy ending.
> The recognised conclusion in the pantomime tradition.

But now, because of Squire Gray, we are in this position!
To have this gloomy ending would be nothing short of tragic.
It seems the only thing to do is introduce some magic.
And with that neat injection we'll achieve what had been planned.
This is where the Fairy Queen can lend a useful hand!

Fairy Queen moves back, hiding. Enter Lily White, downcast, stage right

Lily White

For me the outlook's gloomy. I have no prospects now.
Haven't any assets. First of all I lost me cow.
After that I lost me family, me two lads, Jack and Matt.
Very soon I'll lose me home. No wonder I feel flat!

Fairy Queen advances on Lily White, startling her

Fairy Queen

I'm here to give you something...

Lily White

You did. It was a shock.
But never mind, I'd like to say, that is a lovely frock.
I'm not my usual self today. My nerves are in a state.
I must have forgotten, it is our Annual Fete.
I see you are an entry in the Fancy Dress Parade.
That's a smashing outfit - surely not home-made?

Fairy Queen

You are quite mistaken. I am not what you suppose.

Lily White

Who are you?

Fairy Queen

I am Fairy Queen...

Lily White

Cor! Stone the blooming crows!

Fairy Queen

Yes, I had a feeling that would cause surprise.
You need my assistance - Lily, close your eyes.

Lily White closes her eyes

You will slumber gently, afterwards you'll wake.
Wishes I will grant you - the first three that you make.
I give you assurance will come true today.
(to audience) The task is now completed. I need no longer stay.

Fairy Queen exits, stage right. Lily opens her eyes, looking and moving about. Enter Alice and Rose, stage right

Lily White

Alice, Rose, where did she go? She's vanished out of sight.
I didn't see which way she went. I had me eyes shut tight.
You must have seen here, she was here...

Alice

Who was? Who do you mean?

Lily White

The one who said she'd help me...

Rose

Who did?

Lily White

The Fairy Queen!
Three wishes I'm to be allowed. That's what I heard her say...

Alice

Three wishes! Lily, are you sure?

Lily White

Yes, they'll come true today.

Rose

Lily, you said you're eyes were shut. I think the explanation
Is you dozed off and had a dream. It was imagination.

Alice

Rose, I think we should stay with Lily for the present.

Lily White

Ta very much. I would like that, because it would be pleasant.
At home I feel so lonely, I'm missing Matt and Jack.

Rose

We know you must be Lily...

Lily White

I wish they could come back.
There's no way they can do that now the beanstalk has been
grounded...

Enter Jack and Matt, running, stage right

Jack

Hello Mother...

Matt

Hello Ma...

Lily White

They've done it, I'm astounded!

Alice

We thought you both were stranded, and we'd not see you again.

Rose

How did you get back here, we would like you to explain?

Jack

We found the Giant's castle, we met Princess Mirabel.

Matt

And her maid, called Adelaide, who was up there as well.

Jack

To get back to the beanstalk we had to make a dash,
Because the Giant was chasing us, and then, there was a flash.
Suddenly we found ourselves back on the Village Green.

Matt

We don't know how it happened...

Lily White

I do! The Fairy Queen!
Alice, Rose, if you remember, I wished that Matt and Jack,
Could return from Cloudland - here they are - they have come
back!

Jack

Mother, we are grateful, we're glad we have returned.
We've come back empty-handed, that reward we haven't earned.
The Princess is still in Cloudland, up there in the sky.

Lily White

Jack, to make another wish, that is what I'll try.
You and Matt deserve it, that reward should come to you.
So stand by everybody, here comes wish number two.
I wish Princess Mirabel, and Adelaide, her maid,
Down to Earth from Cloudland, both are now conveyed.

They all look around expectantly, but nothing happens

I didn't get three wishes, that one was a failure.

Matt

Ma, they could have lost their way - and landed in Australia!

Jack

You did your best to help us, the reward we cannot get.
As a family we're united...

Lily White

And we still can't pay that debt.

*Squire Gray is heard shouting off stage. Mirabel and Adelaide are heard
screaming, and all attention is turned towards stage left*

Squire Gray

(off) Get out! Get out of my estate!

Rose

That sounds like Squire Gray...

Squire Gray

Go on! Push off! Get out of here! I'll help you on your way!

Squire Gray enters, stage left, pushing on Princess Mirabel and Adelaide

I do not allow intruders to enter my estate.
Nobody has permission. I will not tolerate
Avon ladies, busy-bodies, wanting me to sign petitions,
Earnest pamphlet-pushers sent on doorstep missions,
Various inspectors, and charity fund-raisers,
Particularly unwelcome are persistent double-glazers!
Nobody is welcome. Everybody can keep out.
Including the lot of you. Clear off, don't hang about.

Squire Gray exits, stage left

Jack

Princess, up there in Cloudland we thought you would remain.

Mirabel

Jack! How pleased I am to know that we have met again.
I have to say I am confused, the castle wall we neared,
We were all together, then you two disappeared!

Adelaide

The Giant was close behind us. It was very frightening.
Suddenly there was a flash, I thought it was lightning!

Mirabel

Everything became transformed. Almost immediately
There we were, on that estate, standing by a tree.

Adelaide

And that nasty man ran up, pushing us about...

Mirabel

He was most disagreeable. Behaving like a lout.

Jack

He is the local Squire, Princess. Bad-tempered, seldom happy.

Matt

In this village we know he's an irritating chappie.

Alice

He's bombastic, anti-social...

Rose

Never friendly, always rude...

Lily White

I for one, wish Squire Gray would change his attitude

Jack

Yes, all of us would like to see a different Squire Gray...

Enter Squire Gray, stage left, smiling broadly

Squire Gray

My friends! How nice to see you. I wish you all "good day".
Why don't you come in my estate? In future it will be
Turned into a Public Park - for the community.

I've been a menace in the past, I want to make amends.
Instead of making enemies, from now on I'll make friends.

Alice

Lily, you wished that he would change, and that wish has come true.
It was no coincidence - so did the other two.

Rose

There must have been a Fairy Queen. It was no imagination.

Lily White

She came to our assistance, let's show our appreciation.

All on stage cheer and clap. Enter Fairy Queen, stage right

Fairy Queen

Thank you! I am flattered by this cordial reception.
I averted a disaster with a magical injection.
As Fairy Queen it is my job to see that wrongs are righted.
It's happened here I'm pleased to say, and everyone's delighted.
(to audience) The happy ending we have reached,
In this our pantomime.
All that's left for me to do is make the final rhyme...

All on stage form into a line

I made the first, and now I make, what is the very last,
This farewell bow we make to you, the members of the cast.

All on stage bow

ALADDIN

CHARACTERS

THE PRESENTER	Who introduces the scenes
ALADDIN	Our intrepid hero
WISHEE	His brother
WIDOW TWANKEE	Their mother - a Pekin laundress
ABENAZER	Their wicked uncle
HI-WUN	Emperor of China
HI-TU	The Empress
PRINCESS LUV-LEE	Their self-willed daughter
CHEE-KEE	Her maid
CHOP-SUEY	The Imperial Executioner
THE GENI OF THE LAMP	An off-stage voice

SCENES

1.	**A STREET IN OLD PEKIN**	Way back in the past
2.	**INSIDE THE DREADSOME CAVERN**	Not long afterwards
3.	**IN WIDOW TWANKEE'S LAUNDRY**	Shortly after that
4.	**IN THE IMPERIAL PALACE**	A week later
5.	**OUTSIDE ALADDIN'S MANSION**	A month later
6.	**TO THE IMPERIAL PALACE AGAIN**	That same day

ALADDIN

Scene 1

A street in Old Pekin. Enter the Presenter

Presenter
> There's a taste of Eastern Promise in the tale we'll tell to you.
> A story to be told to you in rhyme.
> But your minds you'll have to cast back to China, in the past.
> Which is the setting for this pantomime.
> Now, I'll be popping in like this, to introduce each scene,
> I'm Presenter, that's a kind of commentator,
> And here's where we begin, in a street in Old Pekin.
> That's my introduction, see you later!

Presenter exits. Enter Aladdin and Wishee, carrying a basket of laundry, which they put down

Aladdin
> I'm Aladdin...
Wishee
> I'm his brother...
Aladdin and **Wishee**
> *(together, encouraging audience to "Aah")* We've got no Dad,
> But we've a Mother!

Abenazer enters behind them, listening

> She's a local washer-woman...
Wishee
> A Bold and Persil slosher-woman!
> And anything from sheet to hanky can be washed by Widow
> Twankee.

Abenazer moves forward to join them

Abenazer
> I overheard that conversation. Good Morning, I am your relation.
> Your long-lost Uncle, Abenazer, because my brother was your farzer!
Aladdin and **Wishee**
> *(together)* Our FARZER?

Abenazer

(to audience) Well, can anybody down there find a rhyme for
Abenazer?
(now to the brothers) I have a little undertaking,
For which some money you'll be making.

Wishee

I'm all for that, we'll work for you. Uncle, tell us what to do.

Abenazer

No my lad, the task in hand, and I hope you'll understand,
Requires just one, and that's your brother.

Aladdin

(indicating the laundry) Wishee, take that home to Mother.
Explain what's happening, be a pal,
Would you do that...

Wishee

Right-o Al.

Wishee picks up the laundry and exits. Abenazer draws Aladdin closer

Abenazer

There's a place that we'll be seeking, in the hills just outside Pekin.
In a cavern near the road, secret treasure has been stowed.

Aladdin

(excited) Treasure, hidden in a cave?

Abenazer

(quietening him and looking round) Shhh! That's no way to behave!
Aladdin we must be discreet, not shout about it in the street!

Aladdin

Uncle I apologise...

Abenazer

(sizing him up) You'd be just about right-size.
The entrance to the cave's not wide - means I cannot get inside.
(patting his round figure) But some-one slender, just like you,
Can very easily get through.

Aladdin

To help you Uncle, I agree...

Abenazer

Good. Aladdin, come with me.

They both exit. Enter the Presenter

Presenter

Poor Aladdin! He's too trusting. He is being led astray.
Like an innocent bystander, or a dupe.
He should have been more wise, and he'll quickly realise,
When he finds that he's been landed in the soup!

Out beyond the Pekin walls, the pair of them have gone.
Scene Two is in that cavern, which is dread-some.
Aladdin's gone inside, through that gap not very wide.
Which Abenazer couldn't manage - 'cos he's spread-some!

Indicates stomach, then exits

Scene 2

Inside the Dreadsome Cavern. Abenazer remains off stage, out of sight of the audience. Enter Aladdin

Aladdin
Uncle, what is here concealed?
Abenazer
A secret, cannot be revealed!
Aladdin
I don't know what I'm looking for. There's nothing here, of that I'm sure.
I've searched this cave. I've looked all round it...
Abenazer
(angrily) Then look again, until you've found it!
Aladdin
But what am I supposed to find? If only it could be defined.
In here it's cold, and dark, and damp. All I can find is this - a lamp!

He discovers and holds up an old hurricane lamp

Abenazer
That's it! The lamp! My legacy! Come on! Come on! GIVE IT TO ME!
Aladdin
Uncle, there's no need to shout. You'll have the lamp when I get out.
Abenazer
I want it NOW! Without delay. Aladdin, you'll do what I say.
Aladdin
When I come out, and not before...
Abenazer
Then you'll stay there for evermore!
Upon you I will cast a spell. This cave to be your PRISON CELL!

He laughs evilly, the sound gradually fading away to indicate that the cave is closing

Aladdin

Uncle must be a magician! He's put me in this dire position.
This is grave - could not be graver. To think that I did him a favour.
(looking at the lamp) I wonder why he got so shirty?
Over this, it's old and dirty.
He called this treasure, it's appalling...

Rubs lamp on his sleeve. Geni replies off stage, audibly, but not too loud

Geni

Master, I can hear you calling.

Aladdin

(surprised) I'm certain that a voice I heard.
But I'm alone. It's quite absurd.
No-one else in this location...

Geni

It's not your imagination.
I'm here, inside the lamp - a Geni...

Aladdin

(peering closely at lamp) If you are, you must be teeny!

Geni

Master, what I say is true. Allow me to explain to you.
This is a magic lamp you hold. More valuable than jewels or gold
And when rubbed in a certain way, the holder's wishes I obey.

Aladdin

So this is Abenazer's treasure...

Geni

Tell me Master, what's your pleasure?
For you are Master, I am slave...

Aladdin

I wish to get out of this cave.

Geni

A simple task which I will do. The cave is open, so go through.

Aladdin exits with the lamp. Enter the Presenter

Presenter

Wishee went back home with all the laundry.
Told his Mother what had come to pass.
Widow Twankee, when she learned, was worried and concerned.
She knows Abenazer's a snake-in-the-grass!
So here's Scene Three - in Widow Twankee's laundry.
But for the present there's no laundry being done.
She has left her washing-tub, and the clothes she has to scrub,
As she hears what happened to her other son. *(exits)*

Scene 3

In Widow Twankee's Laundry. Enter Widow Twankee, talking, followed by Aladdin with the lamp, and Wishee

Widow Twankee
>You say he locked you in a cave. Abenazer always was a knave.
>He is rotten to the core. I've never liked my Broth'r-in-Law!

Wishee
>Al, how did you get out again?

Aladdin
>That's quite easy to explain. *(holds up lamp)*
>Uncle's treasure was my aid. And a quick escape I made.

Wishee
>Treasure? That's not worth a lot...

Aladdin
>For giving light - well no it's not.
>But back home I've had to bring it...

Wishee
>Then in the dust-bin you should sling it!

Aladdin
>If I did that, it would be tragic, because you see, this lamp is magic!

Widow Twankee
>Magic? Aladdin, are you serious?

Wishee
>Ma, I think that Al's delirious!

Aladdin
>With this a Geni I can summon...

Widow Twankee
>A Geni? Well now, that's a rum 'un!

Aladdin
>I make a wish - he does my bidding...

Wishee
>Come on Al, stop all this kidding.

Aladdin
>*(rubbing the lamp)* Geni, prove that you exist...

Geni
>Master, I'm happy to assist!

Reactions from Widow Twankee and Wishee

Aladdin
>I think I've proved it's efficacious...

Wishee
>Fantastic Al!

Widow Twankee

Well! Goodness gracious!

Aladdin

As long as this lamp I retain, anything I wish - I gain.
An Imperial Declaration is currently in circulation
From the Emperor, no less, to say that Luv-Lee, the Princess,
Is a wedding candidate...

Widow Twankee

In other words, she wants a mate!

Aladdin

With lamp and Geni on my side, the Princess will become my bride.
Our future now could not be finer. We'll be the richest folks in China!

They all exit. Enter the Presenter

Presenter

The Emperor of China, at this time, is called Hi-Wun.
And the Empress, as his wife, is called Hi-Tu.
Their eligible daughter, is full of regal hauteur,
Now her matrimonial prospects are in view.
That Imperial Declaration has been sent out far and wide
Sev'ral thousand copies are in circulation.
With such blanket-advertising, it is not all that surprising,
That Aladdin has received the information.
The response to date has been quite overwhelming.
Prospective suitors have been coming by the score.
But not one has been selected, ev'ry one has been rejected.
So, let's see what will happen in Scene Four!

Presenter exits

Scene 4

In the Imperial Palace. Hi-Wun and Hi-Tu enter, followed by Luv-Lee, moving to sit on three draped chairs. Chee-Kee enters behind them and stands nearby

Hi-Wun

I suppose again today, more applicants we must survey.
Keeping up the same routine!

Hi-Tu

At least a hundred we have seen.

Hi-Wun

They have come and they have gone...

Luv-Lee

So far, not one has turned me on!
Hasn't come up to my rating...

Hi-Wun

Chee-Kee, are there any others waiting?

Chee-Kee

Only one.

Hi-Wun

So, let's begin. Chee-Kee go and show him in.

Chee-Kee exits

Hi-Tu

Luv-Lee you know you can't deny, you are setting sights too high.
What type of groom do you desire...

Luv-Lee

One who'll set my heart on fire!

Hi-Tu

Let's hope that you find him ducky. Only wish I'd been that lucky.
Your father barely lit a spark...

Hi-Wun

Hi-Tu, that's an unkind remark!
My reputation you are slating...

Chee-Kee enters with Abenazer

Chee-Kee

The candidate who has been waiting.

Abenazer bows low in front of Hi-Tu

Abenazer

I've travelled far, but I declare, I never saw a face more fair.
Behold those lips, behold those eyes. Truly I look on Paradise.
What radiance now lights my life...

Hi-Wun

(indignantly) Do you mind - that is my wife!
(indicating Luv-Lee) There is the one you should address.
Our daughter, Luv-Lee, the Princess.

Abenazer now moves to bow low in front of Luv-Lee

Abenazer

I've travelled far, but I declare, I never saw a face more fair.
Behold those lips, behold those eyes...

Luv-Lee
No further need to itemise.
Just cut out this soft soap stuff. From you I have heard enough.
Abenazer
Princess, don't overlook my wooing...
Luv-Lee
Not int'rested. There's nothing doing.
Hi-Wun
Luv-Lee, he has such charming ways...
Hi-Tu
And delightful turn of phrase.
Spoken with a silvery tongue...
Luv-Lee
(yawning) He's far too fat, and far from young.
Chee-Kee, you can show him out...
Abenazer
(shaking his fist at her) You'll be sorry, Princess, never doubt.
Hear this promise I now make, revenge upon you I will take.

Abenazer exits, shaking his fist, followed by Chee-Kee

Hi-Wun
Luv-Lee, you're too selective...
Hi-Tu
Yes, compromise, now - be objective.
Luv-Lee
To compromise I'm not inclined. I know a husband I will find.
A suitor who I can admire. One who'll be my heart's desire.
I hear bells - a tinkling tune. Just like it is in Mills and Boon!
Hi-Tu
Hi-Wun, she's getting starry-eyed...

Chee-Kee enters

Chee-Kee
Another candidate outside. Waiting in the corridor...
Luv-Lee
He'll be the mixture as before. And have nothing going for him...
Hi-Wun
Even so, we can't ignore him. If we did it might upset him...
Hi-Tu
That's true. Chee-Kee, go and get him.

Chee-Kee exits

Hi-Wun

    Will he be like all the rest? Will Luv-Lee be un-impressed?

    Or to him will she take a shine...

Hi-Tu

    Your guess is as good as mine.

Luv-Lee

    Be another waste of time. I doubt if those bells will chime.

    Probably another Wally - a wimp - a yuk - a drip...

Chee-Kee enters with Aladdin. Luv-Lee stands up quickly

    OH! GOLLY!

Surprised reactions from Hi-Wun and Hi-Tu

Hi-Wun

    I have more than just an inkling,

    Luv-Lee's hearing those bells tinkling.

Luv-Lee moves towards Aladdin

Hi-Tu

    Yes, I'm sure she is enthralled.

    Young man, by what name are you called?

Aladdin

    I am Aladdin, from Pekin. Your daughter's hand I'm here to win.

Hi-Wun

    I'd say you've won...

Hi-Tu

    No competition. Aladdin, you've achieved - ignition!

    All those others you've outclassed...

Hi-Wun

    An Imperial Wedding Day, at last!

They all exit. The Presenter enters

Presenter

    So they married and are living in a mansion in Pekin,

    Where the Princess has kept Chee-Kee as her maid.

    Widow Twankee lives next door, with Wishee, they're not poor,

    They're also rich, thanks to the Geni's aid.

    But lurking in the background is the villain of the piece,

    Again into the story he'll arrive.

    Abenazer, crafty man, has devised an evil plan.

    What it is you'll find out in Scene Five. *(exits)*

Scene 5

Outside Aladdin's mansion. Enter Abenazer, wearing a hood and carrying a torch

Abenazer

(lifting hood) Yes, Abenazer, I'm disguised.
In case I should be recognised.
A cunning plan I have, no less, to kidnap that stuck-up Princess.
Aladdin's life will be in ruins - thanks to my nefarious doin's!
(chuckling evilly) You can boo, and you can hiss.
I don't mind, I'm used to this.
I'm a bad 'un, through and through. And I can hiss and boo at you!

Abenazer interacts with the audience. Finally he raises his hand

We all enjoyed that, did we not? However, to get back to the plot.
I will put my plan in action, offering unique attraction.
(calling out) If you've a lamp that is an old one,
Not a silver or a gold one.
I'll exchange it here today. For a new one, you don't pay.
But bring the old lamp out to me. And get a new one from me -
FREE!

Chee-Kee enters with lamp

Chee-Kee

What's the catch in what you say...

Abenazer

No catch! I'm changing lamps today.
Straightforward swap, I will arrange it...

Chee-Kee

This old lamp. Will you exchange it? It's useless, no illumination.

Abenazer

(flashing the torch) Then look at this...

Chee-Kee

It's a sensation!

Abenazer

With one of these you can't go wrong.
(flashes torch again) Made by craftsmen in Hong Kong.

They exchange lamp and torch

Chee-Kee

(flashing torch) It's fantastic! It's sensational!

A lamp that's fully operational!

Chee-Kee exits, still flashing the torch

Abenazer

And operational I shall be. The time for vengeance comes to me!
And I'll strike within the hour. Now Abenazer has the power.

Abenazer exits, chuckling evilly. Enter the Presenter

Presenter

This plan of Abenazer's is a devastating one.
An evil scheme consid'rably far-sighted.
Rendered worthless at a stroke, completely stony-broke,
Aladdin's cosy life-style will be blighted!
His mansion, and the Princess, and Chee-Kee in fact - the lot!
Simply vanished. Disappeared into thin air.
By the Emperor arrested, Aladdin took offence, protested.
Complaining that such treatment was unfair.

Presenter sets two draped chairs, then exits

Scene 6

*The Imperial Palace again. Enter Hi-Wun and Hi-Tu who sit on the chairs.
They are followed by Aladdin and Chop-Suey, who carries an axe and a
basket*

Hi-Wun

At your wedding we were sure, you'd be a perfect son-in-law.
Now all you own has disappeared...

Hi-Tu

You must admit, it's rather weird!

Hi-Wun

A matter of great consternation. And we demand an explanation.

Aladdin

I told you, the fault's not mine. I went out, everything was fine.
When I returned - nothing there! Except a lot of empty air!
It's a mystery, I confess...

Hi-Wun

Perhaps, but you've lost a Princess.
And irrespective of the reason, in China, that's an Act of Treason!
For which there must be retribution, which for you means -
execution!

Chop-Suey steps forward, putting down basket

Chop-Suey

Citizen, you've come a cropper, and have to meet my chippy-chopper!
(displaying axe) My axe is sharp, the edge is keen, a single stroke...
(demonstrating a swing) A head off - clean!
I guarantee a perfect job, when I am taking off a nob!

Hi-Tu

Oh dear! That made me feel quite ill...

Hi-Wun

We do not underrate your skill.

Chop-Suey

Well, I'm an expert. I never botch it...

Hi-Tu

I really do not want to watch it!

Aladdin

And I don't want to lose my head - can't I do something else instead?

Hi-Wun

By you a pardon can be earned - if our daughter is returned.

Aladdin

I do not know where I could start...

Hi-Wun

Then with your head you'll have to part.

Hi-Tu

It seems a pity, such a shame...

Widow Twankee and Wishee hurry in

Widow Twankee

(aggressively) Hang on a minute, what's your game?
Looks like we got here just in time...

Wishee

Al, what's all this about some crime?
In which we've heard you're implicated...

Aladdin

(pointing to Hi-Wun and Hi-Tu) They say I must be liquidated!

Chop-Suey

His execution's imminent...

Aladdin

They won't believe I'm innocent! I do not deserve this slaughter...

Hi-Wun

Yes you do - you've lost our daughter.

Hi-Tu

But there could be a change of mind, if our daughter you can find.
Bring her back as good as new...

Widow Twankee

Oh well, that's something I can do. Aladdin's head, no need to chop it.

(dismissive gesture to Chop-Suey) As for you chum, you can hop it!

Hi-Wun

May I remind you, I'm boss here...

Hi-Tu

(smiling) I like to let you think so dear.

Hi-Wun

Executioner, you remain. We could be needing you again.

(to Widow Twankee) If your claim cannot be proved,

Then, three heads will be removed.

Wishee

I hope Ma you know what you're doing.

If not there could be trouble brewing.

Widow Twankee

Nothing to it, just a doddle! None of us will lose a noddle.

Abenazer is to blame. I'll show him two can play his game.

So I made some preparation. Stand back for a demonstration.

(putting on a pair of large, comic spectacles) Testing, testing,

One, two, three. Geni, are you receiving me?

Geni

(off stage) Even though I am not near you.

We have contact, I can hear you.

Your instructions I am waiting, now we are communicating.

Hi-Wun

This is odd...

Hi-Tu

Indeed it is...

Widow Twankee

Bring to Aladdin, what is his.

The magic lamp to him restore, situation as before.

Make Abenazer take a stroll - all the way to the North Pole.

For in that place that I have chosen, his assets will be firmly frozen.

And make sure he stays that way...

Geni

As you command, so I obey.

Luv-Lee and Chee-Kee enter. Chee-Kee has the lamp which she gives to Aladdin. Hi-Wun and Hi-Tu look amazed

Hi-Wun

Luv-Lee is back, it's no illusion...

Hi-Tu

I have reached the same conclusion.

Aladdin

    Mother, just how did you do it...

Widow Twankee

    Aladdin, there was nothing to it.

    I took the lamp. just for a minute, chatted to the Geni in it.

    An arrangement we both made, if any time I wanted aid,

    (indicating spectacles) Electronic apparatus,

    Of Special Secret Agent status.

    So we could communicate, as you saw me demonstrate.

Hi-Wun

    A clever parent there you've got.

    One who obviously knows what's what.

Hi-Tu

    Through her a dreadful wrong was righted...

Aladdin

    With Luv-Lee I am re-united.

Widow Twankee

    A case of happy families, everyone up here agrees. *(nods of approval)*

    More or less, that's all there is, except this final bit of biz.

Enter Abenazer and Geni, holding card saying "Geni's voice". They are followed by the Presenter

Presenter

    We hope we've entertained you with our potted pantomime.

    It is over, we have nothing more to tell.

    And the time has come when now, we make our final bow,

    And so, to all of you we say...

All

    (bowing) Farewell!